A boy called Elton

A boy called Elton

A Popjustice Book
Illustrated by David Whittle

First published in Great Britain in 2006 by Friday Books
An imprint of The Friday Project Limited
83 Victoria Street, London SW1H 0HW

www.thefridayproject.co.uk
www.fridaybooks.co.uk

Text © Peter Robinson 2006
Illustrations © David Whittle 2006

ISBN – 10 1 905548 08 7
ISBN – 13 978 1 905548 08 8

British Library Cataloguing in Publication Data

A catalogue record for this book is available
from the British Library

Designed and produced by Staziker Jones
www.stazikerjones.co.uk

The Publisher's policy is to use paper
manufactured from sustainable sources

This book belongs to

_____

I am ____ years old

My favourite Elton song is ———————

When I grow up, I want to be ————————

Here is my autograph!

_____

Pop!
justice
idols

This is Elton.

Elton is a very famous singer of songs.

As well as singing songs, Elton writes them too!

Clever Elton.

Elton likes to go shopping.

He does not really mind what he buys and it does not matter anyway because he has so much money.

Sometimes Elton gets very grumpy with people – and when he is grumpy with people he tells them exactly why!

For example, once Elton was very mean about a girl called Madonna.

He said that Madonna should not make people pay to watch her pretend to sing songs!

Elton was very angry about this. He was so angry his head almost fell off!

Elton was born in England a long time ago.

It was just after a very big war, and people were still tidying up.

When he was a little boy, Elton had a different name. He was called Reginald.

Reginald is a bad name for a popstar so when he was older he changed it.

Little Elton liked to play the piano.

Even though he had very small fingers,
he was so good at it that he was allowed
to play the piano in a pub.

He was paid about 1p every time he played the
piano. You cannot buy many flowers with 1p!

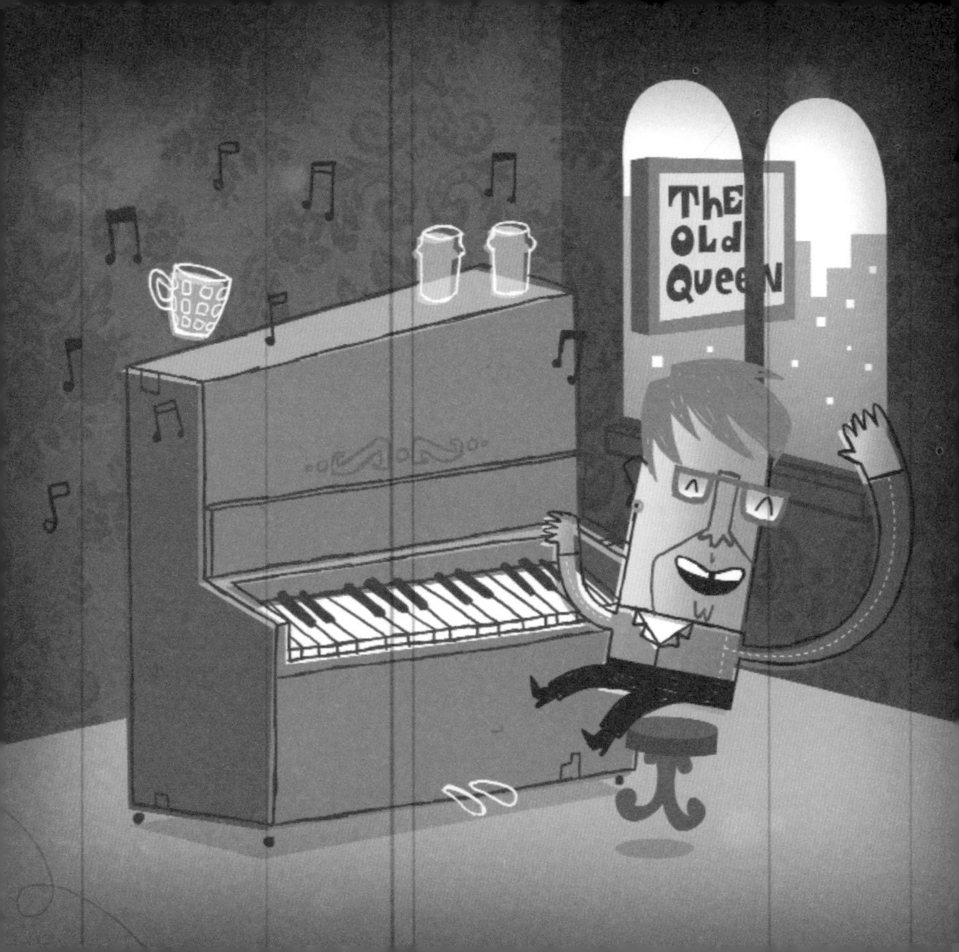
ThE OLd QuEEN

This made Elton very popular, and it cheered him up because sometimes he was sad about not looking like a famous film star.

To cheer Elton up even more, a special school for gifted musicians said they would like Elton to be a pupil.

It was a school for boys with lots of money, but they let Elton in for free.

Elton was very good at writing songs. But there was a problem – Elton could only write half a song.

One day he met a boy called Bernie. Bernie could only write half a song too, but when you put Elton's half songs together with Bernie's half songs they sounded very nice.

Elton and Bernie made friends with each other and decided to write lots of whole songs.

It was not long before Elton and Bernie met a man called Dick.

Dick worked with a very famous band called The Beatles and he said he could help make Elton famous too.

Because Elton liked Dick, Elton said yes to Dick, and Dick changed Elton's life.

Elton became one of the most famous singers of songs in the whole wide world!

He also discovered that dressing up in funny costumes made him happy.

Special sweets and special fizzy pop drinks also made Elton very happy.

Unfortunately, sometimes he would eat and drink too many sweets and fizzy pop, and they made him feel unwell.

One day he had to make the very difficult decision not to eat all those sweets. He has been happier ever since!

Elton has always been a big fan of football.

Despite this, his favourite football team is Watford FC.

One day he gave them lots of money and decided to be in charge.

They won some matches, all thanks to Elton!

In 1976, Elton told the world one of his secrets.

He said that instead of loving ladies, he loved men instead.

Because it was the olden days, some people did not realise that this was alright.

In fact, it made some silly people stop buying Elton's records!

Fortunately, a few years later, Elton decided he did not only love men after all.

He fell in love with a lady called Renate, and they got married.

Elton wore a pink hat and a pink tie to the wedding – it looked like they would be happy forever!

Unfortunately, Elton and Renate eventually stopped loving each other, but they stayed friends.

In 1991, Elton invented a special organization. It was to help people who were very sick and to stop people getting sick in the first place.

Elton's new company was called the Elton John AIDS Foundation

It has helped lots of people ever since.

Thank you Elton!

One day Elton decided to write a song about a lion.

The song was called 'Circle Of Life'.

It was about lions being born and then lions dying.

It is always very sad when a lion dies.

On a very sad day, Elton's very good friend Diana had a terrible accident.

Unfortunately she died. This made Elton very upset.

He recorded a special a song for her, called 'Candle In The Wind 1997'. The point of the song was that candles do not last very long in the wind.

That is why they invented torches.

32 million people bought the song, even though it made them cry.

Imagine how many people might have bought it if it had been a happy song!

The Queen Of England liked Elton because he was so nice to so many people.

The Queen decided to give Elton a present – another new name! From now on, he would be known as Sir Elton.

This was supposed to be a nice thing but it just meant that all Elton's friends had to change his name in their mobile phones.

In 2005, Sir Elton and his boyfriend, a boy called David, decided to get married.

They looked so happy.

Unfortunately, one newspaper wrote a story about it and they put 'Elton takes David up the aisle!' at the top.

It was a joke because some people thought it was funny that men loved each other.

The silly newspaper still thought it was 1976!

So that is the story of a boy called Elton.

Maybe you can grow up to be just like him –
but you'll have to practice very hard at piano
playing and shopping!

Elton John and the Queen both wear very big dresses.

Cut around the edges (be careful with the scissors!) and act out special scenes.

Elton: In these heels I'm worried I might fall over and collide with one of your priceless paintings.
The Queen: Don't go breaking my art.

Have fun!

justice idols

Loads more Popjustice Idols are waiting to say hello to you in your local bookshop - including Robbie Williams, Britney Spears, Eminem, Pete Doherty, Michael Jackson, Elton John, Take That and Madonna!

www.popjustice.com/idols

PLUS!

THE WEBSITE!

Daily updates, podcasts, videos, downloads, pop gossip, pop stuff, pop in general... Plus get Popjustice on your mobile phone!

www.popjustice.com

THE ALBUM!

The greatest pop album of all time, featuring AMAZING songs by AMAZING popstars, all mixed nicely together!

www.popjustice.com/album

THE CLUB NIGHT!

Two floors of unbelievable pop music, every week, in the centre of London town. We do not play stuff by Shayne Ward!

www.popjustice.com/club